Can Jodie Find It?

written by Ana Conrad

illustrated by Cathy Morrison

Mc Graw Hill **Macmillan McGraw-Hill**

New York   Farmington

There is no more room in Jodie's
room! She has so many things.
Jodie likes having this kind of
room. But sometimes she can't
find the things she needs.

Jodie has to play in a big game
today. She has to leave by one
o'clock. But Jodie can't find her
clock. She could ask her mom to
tell her the time. But she wants
to find her clock.

"I will use my ears to find my
clock," says Jodie. "I will listen
for the tick, tock of the clock.
Then I will find it."

Jodie hears the tick, tock of the
clock. Where is it? Jodie stands
still. Then she sees the clock.
Jodie is glad she found it.

Jodie needs her ball to play in
the game. It is up on a high shelf.
Jodie can see the shelf, but she
can't see the ball.

"I will find it by using my fingers,"
says Jodie. Jodie stands on her
toes. Her fingers feel for the ball.

Jodie feels something round.
She has it!

"Where is the bowl of popcorn I
gave you?" asks Jodie's mom.
Jodie looks around. She does not
see the bowl.

"I used my ears to find the clock,"
says Jodie. "I used my fingers to
find the ball."

"Now I will use my nose to find
the bowl of popcorn," says Jodie.
Jodie sniffs high and low.

"It is under my coat," says Jodie.

"How did it get under my coat?"

"Don't forget your sneakers," says
Jodie's mom. "You will need them
for the game."

"I don't see them," says Jodie.
"I will have to find them."

"I can't use my ears to find them,"
says Jodie. "I can't use my nose
to find them. I will have to use my
fingers again. And I know where
to begin."

Can you see under Jodie's bed?
There are many things under
Jodie's bed. There are all kinds of
games. There are caps and dolls.

And there are sneakers, as well!
Jodie can feel the laces. Jodie can
feel a toe. Jodie gives a tug and
gets them out.

"Now I have my ball and my sneakers," says Jodie. "I think it is time for me to leave. But I can't find my clock again!"